Move It!

Description

Students explore the phenomena of a toy car on a ramp speeding up, slowing down, and stopping. They read a nonfiction book about forces and explore how pushes and pulls can change motion. Then, they apply their knowledge to complete a design challenge: getting a toy dog (named Newton) into his doghouse!

Alignment With the *Next Generation Science Standards*

Performance Expectations

K-PS2-2: Analyze data to determine if a design solution works as intended to change the speed or direction of an object with a push or a pull.

K-2-ETS1-3: Analyze data from tests of two objects designed to solve the same problem to compare the strengths and weaknesses of how each performs.

Science and Engineering Practices	Disciplinary Core Ideas	Crosscutting Concepts
Analyzing and Interpreting Data Use observations (firsthand or from media) to describe patterns and/or relationships in the natural and designed world(s) in order to answer scientific questions and solve problems. Analyze data from tests of an object or tool to determine if it works as intended. Constructing Explanations and Designing Solutions Use tools and/or materials to design and/or build a device that solves a specific problem or a solution to a specific problem. Generate and/or compare multiple solutions to a problem.	PS2.A: Forces and Motion Pushes and pulls can have different strengths and directions. Pushing or pulling on an object can change the speed or direction of its motion and can start or stop it. ETS1.C: Optimizing the Design Solution Because there is always more than one possible solution to a problem, it is useful to compare and test designs.	Cause and Effect Simple tests can be designed to gather evidence to support or refute student ideas about causes. Scale, Proportion, and Quantity Relative scales allow objects and events to be compared and described (e.g., bigger and smaller, hotter and colder, faster and slower).

Note: The activities in this lesson will help students move toward the performance expectations listed, which is the goal after multiple activities. However, the activities will not by themselves be sufficient to reach the performance expectations.

Featured Picture Books

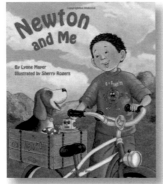

TITLE: **Newton and Me**
AUTHOR: **Lynne Mayer**
ILLUSTRATOR: **Sherry Rogers**
PUBLISHER: **Sylvan Dell**
YEAR: **2010**
GENRE: **Story**
SUMMARY: *Named an Outstanding Science Trade Book by the National Science Teaching Association and the Children's Book Council, this rhyming book about a boy and his dog, Newton, provides a fun introduction to forces and motion.*

TITLE: **Move It! Motion, Forces and You**
AUTHOR: **Adrienne Mason**
ILLUSTRATOR: **Claudia Dávila**
PUBLISHER: **Kids Can Press**
YEAR: **2005**
GENRE: **Non-Narrative Information**
SUMMARY: *This fun-to-read and easy-to-understand book provides a simple introduction to forces and motion, with many opportunities to "stop and try it!"*

Time Needed

This lesson will take several class periods. Suggested scheduling is as follows:

Session 1: Engage with Picture Walk Through Newton and Me

Session 2: Explore with Ride, Newton, Ride!

Session 3: Explain with Newton and Me Read-Aloud

Session 4: Explore/Explain with Move It! Read-Aloud and Stop and Try It! Activities

Session 5: Elaborate with Newton's Doghouse Challenge and Evaluate with Our Best Design

Materials

For Ride, Newton, Ride! (per group of 3–4 students)

- 1 small plastic dog figurine (Note: Safari Ltd TOOBS and other brands of dog figurines are available in packs of 12 from many retailers.)
- 1 die-cast metal toy car (such as Hot Wheels or Matchbox)
- 12 in. section of toy-car track to use as a ramp (or use a small wooden ramp)
- Books to change the height of the ramp

2

- Approximately 8 in. square of green felt or textured fabric to represent grass
- 2 plastic bingo markers
- 2 identical 8 oz. rectangular containers with lids, 1 empty and 1 filled with rocks or marbles

For Move It! Read-Aloud

- 3 identical opaque containers with lids 32 oz. or larger (prepared in advance):
    - 1 filled with rocks or marbles
    - 1 filled with uncooked macaroni
    - 1 filled with crumpled paper
- Cotton ball for each student
- Straw for each student
- Cutting board or other item that could be used as a smooth ramp
- Large eraser
- Small stone
- Small wooden block
- Ice cube
- Glue stick

For Newton's Doghouse Challenge (per group of 3–4 students)

- Same dog, car, track, books, felt or fabric, and containers as used in the Ride, Newton, Ride! activities
- Tape
- 16 oz. plastic cup with a half circle cut in the lip that is big enough for Newton and his car to fit through when the cup is upside down
- 12 in. ruler

32 Oz. (1 Liter) Wide Mouth High Density Polyethylene (HDPE) White Plastic Jars with Pressurized Screw Top Lid can be found at Amazon.com.

Student Pages

- Ride, Newton, Ride!
- Our Best Design
- STEM Everywhere

Background for Teachers

This lesson provides students with opportunities to recognize the simple cause-and-effect relationships between forces and motion. The Framework suggests that in early grades students

experience the phenomenon that pushes and pulls can be used to change the motion of an object—to make it go faster or slower, change direction, start moving, or stop moving. Students explore what happens when toy cars travel down ramps, move across different surfaces, and bump into objects of different weights. These explorations give them the opportunity to observe the effects of pushes, pulls, gravity, and friction. Students learn that forces are pushes and pulls and can make objects start moving, slow down, speed up, change direction, or stop moving. Gravity is a force that pulls everything down toward the center of Earth. Friction is a force that occurs when two objects rub together. Friction can slow down an object that is moving. For example, when a toy car rolls from a tile floor onto a piece of felt, the car slows down because of the increased friction created by the rougher surface. Although the terms gravity and friction are mentioned in this lesson during the read-aloud and activities, students do not need to memorize the terms and their definitions. Rather, they experience these two forces during their hands-on activities, observe how they affect the motion of a toy car, and then use these forces to change the motion of an object in a design challenge. This lesson explores basic cause-and-effect relationships between forces and motion. Once cause-and-effect relationships are recognized, students can begin to predict and explain events in new circumstances and apply their scientific understandings to solving problems. In this lesson, students apply what they have learned to complete a simple design challenge.

Note: The activities in this lesson are ideally done on tile floors. If your classroom floors are carpeted, try to find other areas in your school that have smooth-surface floors, such as the hallways, gymnasium, or cafeteria.

Learning Progressions

Below are the DCI grade band endpoints for grades K–2 and 3–5. These are provided to show how student understanding of the DCIs in this lesson will progress in future grade levels.

DCIs	Grades K–2	Grades 3–5
PS2.A: Forces and Motion	• Pushes and pulls can have different strengths and directions. • Pushing or pulling on an object can change the speed or direction of its motion and can start or stop it.	• Each force acts on one particular object and has both strength and a direction. An object at rest typically has multiple forces acting on it, but they add to give zero net force on the object. Forces that do not sum to zero can cause changes in the object's speed or direction of motion • The patterns of an object's motion in various situations can be observed and measured; when that past motion exhibits a regular pattern, future motion can be predicted from it.
ETS1.C: Optimizing the Design Solution	• Because there is always more than one possible solution to a problem, it is useful to compare and test designs.	• Different solutions need to be tested in order to determine which of them best solves the problem, given the criteria and the constraints.

Source: Willard, T., ed. 2015. The NSTA quick-reference guide to the NGSS: Elementary school. Arlington, VA: NSTA Press.

engage

Picture Walk Through *Newton and Me*

Connecting to the Common Core
Reading: Literature
INTEGRATION OF KNOWLEDGE AND IDEAS: K.7

Inferring

Show students the cover of Newton and Me. Tell them that you are going to take a "picture walk" through the book and you would like them to try to infer what the book is about. As you show the pictures, have them signal when they see an illustration of something moving, such as the truck rolling down the hill, the wagon full of rocks being pulled across the yard, or the ball rolling in the grass. Students will likely recognize that the book is about a boy and his dog observing how ordinary things move.

Show students a small, plastic dog figurine. Tell them that the plastic dog will represent Newton, the dog from the story. This dog is a little bit different from the dog in the story, however, because this dog travels only by car! Then, show them a die-cast metal toy car. Explain that before you read the book to them, they are going to have a chance to experiment with Newton, his car, a ramp made from a toy-car track (or a wooden ramp), some roadblocks (plastic containers), and felt or fabric. Tape the dog securely to the car, and tell students that from now on you will be referring to Newton and the car as Newton's car. Place Newton's car on the floor and ask

? What could we do to cause Newton's car to move? (Students will likely suggest you push it. Push the car and observe its motion.)

? What are some other ways to cause Newton's car to move? (They might say pull it, blow air on it, wave a paper behind it, place it on a ramp, pull it with a magnet, etc.)

? Once Newton's car is moving, how could we make it stop? (Block it with something, put it on a rough surface, etc.)

? How could we make it change direction? (Push it in a different direction, pull it in another direction, etc.)

? How could we make it speed up? (Push harder, make it go down a hill, etc.)

? How could we make it slow down? (Put it on carpet, give it a lighter push, etc.)

> **CCC: Cause and Effect**
> Simple tests can be designed to gather evidence to support or refute student ideas about causes.

explore

Ride, Newton, Ride!

Connecting to the Common Core
Mathematics
MEASUREMENT AND DATA: K.MD.2

Divide students into groups of three to four, and tell them that they are going to make Newton's car move in various ways. Give each group of students a toy car with a plastic dog (Newton) taped onto the car, a 12 in. section of toy-car track to use as a ramp, some books to stack to change the height of the ramp, two plastic bingo markers for marking the car's location, and a copy of the Ride, Newton, Ride! student page. Lead the groups through the following activities, and have them record their results on the student page. At the end of each activity, have each group compare its results with the findings of other groups.

LOW AND HIGH RAMPS

Part A: Low and High Ramps

Have each group make an incline by placing one end of the toy-car track on a book. (A small piece of tape can be used to keep the ramp in place.) Have each group release Newton's car (they should not push it!) from the top of the ramp, observe how fast it moves, and record how far it moves by placing a plastic bingo marker next to where it stops. Ask

? Were you surprised by how far the car went? (Answers will vary.)

? How do you think you could make the car go faster and farther, without pushing it? (Students will likely suggest raising the height of the ramp.)

> **CCC: Scale, Proportion, and Quantity**
> Relative scales allow objects and events to be compared and described (e.g., faster and slower).

Allow students to experiment with changing the height of the ramp. Each time they change the height, they should compare the distance the car rolled to the marker they placed on the first run. Then, ask

? How did changing the height of the ramp affect the distance and speed that Newton traveled?

(Generally, the higher the ramp, the faster and farther the car goes. However, some students will notice that if the ramp becomes too high, the car crashes onto the floor and does not move as far.)

Have students circle their answer in Part A on the student page. They should realize that the car goes faster and farther after going down a higher ramp.

CHANGING THE SURFACE

Part B: Changing the Surface

Give each group a square of felt or textured fabric to place at the end of the ramp. Then, have the students release Newton's car from the top and use a bingo marker to record how far Newton travels. Next, have the students place a smooth surface at the end of the ramp (or let it roll onto the floor if you have tile) and repeat. Have them use the two markers to compare how far the car traveled on each of the two surfaces. Ask

? Did the surface make a difference in how fast and far Newton traveled? (Students should notice that the car moves faster and farther on the smooth surface than it does on the rough surface.)

Have students circle the appropriate answer in Part B on the student page.

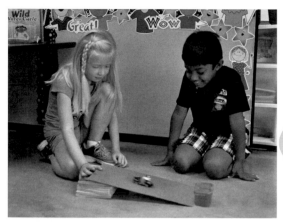

LIGHT WEIGHT VERSUS HEAVY WEIGHT

Part C: Light Weight Versus Heavy Weight

Note: Be sure to try this activity in advance with your materials to determine the best ramp height.

Give each group two identical plastic containers, one that is empty and one that is filled with rocks or marbles. Have each student hold the containers in their hands so they can feel that one is much heavier than the other. Have each group set up a ramp and then place the empty container at the end of the ramp. Have each group release Newton's car from the top of the ramp and mark how far the container moves. Ask

? Did the container move? (Answers will vary.)

? What caused it to move? (the car hitting it)

? What do you think will happen when we do the same thing but replace the lighter container with the heavier container? (Answers will vary.)

> **SEP: Analyzing and Interpreting Data**
> Use observations to describe patterns and relationships in order to answer scientific questions and solve problems.

Have students place the heavier container at the end of the ramp and release the car again. Have them mark how far the heavier container moves. Have students use the two markers to compare how far each container moved. Have them circle their answer in Part C of the student page. Students should notice that the lighter container moves farther than the heavier one.

explain

Newton and Me Read-Aloud

> Connecting to the Common Core
> **Reading: Literature**
> KEY IDEAS AND DETAILS: K.1

Making Connections: Text to Self

Next, tell students that you are going to read the book Newton and Me and you would like them to signal when they hear something in the book that reminds them of one of the activities they did during the Ride, Newton, Ride! activities. When they signal, stop reading and ask them to share their connections. You may want to have a set of the supplies from the explore section above to use as a model during your discussion. Following are some examples:

- Page 6 relates to Part B: "The ball won't roll far in the rough, grassy yard. It rolls much farther on a surface that's smooth and hard." Students should realize that the text and illustration on this page connect with the changing surface activity. The grass is like the felt or fabric they used. Things roll faster and therefore farther on a smooth surface than a rough surface.

- Page 11 relates to Part A: Students should relate the hill on page 11 to the low-and-high ramps activity and realize that the higher the hill, the faster and farther things move as they travel down it.

- Pages 15–17 relate to Part C: They should connect the heavy and light wagons on pages

15–17 to the heavy and light containers in the light weight versus heavy weight activity and recognize that the heavier something is, the harder it is to get it moving.

After reading, tell students that you have a non-fiction book to share with them that will introduce them to some new vocabulary they can use to describe the motion of objects.

explore/explain

Move It! Read-Aloud

Connecting to the Common Core
Reading: Informational Text
KEY IDEAS AND DETAILS: K.3

Ahead of time, gather the materials you need for this read-aloud so that you can easily flow back and forth between activities and explanations from the book (see "Materials" section). Show students the cover of Move It! and introduce the author, Adrienne Mason, and the illustrator, Claudia Dávila. Tell students that this book can help them learn more about forces and motion and the names of some of the different forces they observed when experimenting with Newton. The book is written in an interactive manner. You will be stopping to try different activities and asking questions as you read.

Read the book aloud, pausing to respond to the questions posed by the author and to try the activities that follow.

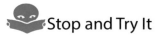 Stop and Try It

"Push It!" Activity

After reading through page 8, "Push It!," get out the three containers filled with rocks or marbles, uncooked macaroni, and crumpled paper, and call on a few students to push the containers. Then, ask

PUSHING THE CONTAINERS

? Which container needed the most force (the biggest push) to move?

? What do you think is in it?

? Which needed the least force (the smallest push) to move?

? What do you think is in it?

> **SEP: Analyzing and Interpreting Data**
> Use observations to describe patterns and relationships in order to answer scientific questions and solve problems.

Remove the lids so that students can check their guesses, and then read the explanation on the page titled "What's Happening?" (p. 14) where students learn that it takes more force to move heavy things and less force to move lighter things.

"Puffing Power" Activity

After reading through pages 14–15, "Puffing Power," give each a student a straw and a cotton ball. (We suggest using a cotton ball instead of a ping pong ball because a cotton ball will not roll around the classroom.) Read through the procedure on page 15, and invite students to try each step. Then, read the explanation on page 15 titled "What's Happening?" where students learn that a smaller force causes the cotton ball to move slowly and a bigger force causes the cotton ball to move faster.

PUFFING POWER

> **CCC: Cause and Effect**
> Simple tests can be designed to gather evidence to support or refute student ideas about causes.

Read pages 16–25, pausing to ask the questions posed by the author. Skip the activity on pages 22–23 because it does not pertain to the activities in the explore phase.

"Sliding Along" Activity

When you get to pages 26–27, "Sliding Along," demonstrate the activity for the class. Follow the instructions step by step, and give students time to respond to the questions. Then, read the explanation on page 27 titled "What's Happening?" where students learn that there is more friction between some materials than others.

Finish reading the rest of the book aloud.

Note: The ideas for parents and teachers shared on pages 30–31 of Move It! are simple ways to explore these concepts further in everyday situations, such as playing on the playground, kicking a ball, kicking a rolling ball to change its direction, dropping objects, lifting things, comparing the surfaces of everyday items, and dragging an object over different surfaces.

SLIDING ALONG

elaborate

Newton's Doghouse Challenge

Challenge students to apply what they have learned about forces and motion to solve a problem. Tell students that Newton is having trouble parking his car in his doghouse without moving the doghouse or knocking it over. He needs their help! Give each group of three to four students a toy dog taped to a toy car, some tape, a piece of felt or fabric, a toy-car track, some books, the two containers of different weights, and a ruler. Make a "doghouse" for each group by cutting an opening in a plastic cup from the lip down (creating the "door"). The opening should be large enough for Newton and the car to go through. Have students place the cup upside down 1 ft. away from the end of the ramp with the door facing the ramp. Their challenge is to use the supplies to get Newton from the top of the ramp into the doghouse without touching the car and without moving the doghouse.

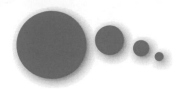

NEWTON'S DOGHOUSE CHALLENGE

Encourage students to use what they learned from the books and activities to set up their design. Tell students that it might take a lot of tries to figure out the challenge. Remind them to not be discouraged if their design doesn't work right way. Remind them that real engineers spend a lot of time trying to figure out how to solve problems! Allow them several attempts, and encourage them to modify their designs until they get one that works. As you visit groups, ask guiding questions, such as the following:

? What could you do to the ramp to make Newton's car go faster and farther or slower and not as far? (Make the ramp higher or lower by adding books.)

? How could you change the surface of what Newton's car is riding on to slow him down? (Place the felt or fabric on or near the ramp or in front of the doghouse.)

? What could you do to make the doghouse harder to move? (Make it heavier by putting the heavy plastic container on top of it.)

SEP: Designing Solutions
Use tools and/or materials to design and build a solution to a specific problem.

Students can solve the problem in three ways. (There are certainly other ways, but these three ways relate to the activities and reading they have done up to this point.) Students can do the following:

1. Change the angle of the ramp (add or remove books from the ramp).
2. Change the surface the car is rolling on (place the felt between the end of the ramp and the doghouse).
3. Make the doghouse heavier (place the heavy plastic container on top of the doghouse).

Their solution will likely be some combination of those three options.

When groups figure out a design that worked, have them demonstrate it for you. Then, ask

? Can you come up with a different way to meet the challenge?

SEP: Designing Solutions
Compare multiple solutions to a problem.

After all groups have successfully met the challenge in at least two different ways, have them discuss what they thought was their best design. Groups should share with the rest of the class by demonstrating their design so that students can see that Newton's car can get into the doghouse multiple ways. Encourage students to compare and contrast the different solutions by asking questions, such as the following:

? What do the different designs have in common? (Answers will vary.)

? What is different about the designs? (Answers will vary.)

? Is there just one way to solve this problem? (No, there are multiple ways to solve a design challenge.)

National Science Teaching Association

evaluate

Our Best Design

Connecting to the Common Core
Writing
TEXT TYPES AND PURPOSES: K.2

Writing

Give each student the Our Best Design student page. Have students draw and label a picture of their team's best design. Their drawings should include Newton's car, the ramp, the doghouse (cup), and any other supplies they used.

Help students reflect on their design by asking questions, such as

? How did you get Newton to start moving? (put him on top of the ramp)

? What force pulled Newton down the ramp? (gravity)

? What did you do to make Newton move faster? (raised the ramp)

? What did you do to make Newton move more slowly? (lowered the ramp, added a rough surface)

? How did you get Newton to stop moving? (put something in front of him, added a rough surface, waited for him to stop)

? What problems did you encounter when designing your solution? (Answers will vary.)

? How did you solve those problems? (Answers will vary.)

? What is another solution you could try that might work? (Answers will vary.)

STEM Everywhere

Give students the STEM Everywhere student page as a way to involve their families and extend their learning. They can do the activity with an adult helper and share their results with the class. If students do not have access to these materials at home, you may choose to have them complete this activity at school.

Opportunities for Differentiated Instruction

This box lists questions and challenges related to the lesson that students may select to research, investigate, or innovate. Students may also use the questions as examples to help them generate their own questions. These questions can help you move your students from the teacher-directed investigation to engaging in the science and engineering practices in a more student-directed format.

Extra Support

For students who are struggling to meet the lesson objectives, provide a question and guide them in the process of collecting research or helping them design procedures or solutions.

Extensions

For students with high interest or who have already met the lesson objectives, have them choose a question (or pose their own question), conduct their own research, and design their own procedures or solutions.

After selecting one of the questions in this box or formulating their own questions, students can individually or collaboratively make predictions, design investigations or surveys to test their predictions, collect evidence, devise explanations, design solutions, or examine related resources. They can communicate their findings through a science notebook, at a poster session or gallery walk, or by producing a media project.

Continued

Opportunities for Differentiated Instruction (*continued*)

Research
Have students brainstorm researchable questions:

? Who was Isaac Newton, and what were some of his discoveries?

? Is the force of gravity different on the Moon?

? Are there other forces at work in the world besides gravity and friction?

Investigate
Have students brainstorm testable questions to be solved through science or math:

? Would adding weight to a toy car make a difference in how far it travels?

? What happens to the distance a toy car travels as you increase the height of the ramp? Is there a limit to how high you can make the ramp before the car falls off?

? Which surface slows the motion of a toy car more: construction paper, felt, or sandpaper?

Innovate
Have students brainstorm problems to be solved through engineering:

? Can you design a way for Newton's car to turn before it goes into the doghouse?

? Can you design a game with the supplies from Newton's Doghouse Challenge?

? Can you design a marble run using a box or piece of cardboard, straws or craft sticks, and tape?

More Books to Read

Bradley, K. B. 2005. *Forces make things move*. New York: HarperTrophy.
Summary: Simple language and comical illustrations show how forces make things move, prevent them from starting to move, and stop them from moving.

Higgins, N. 2009. *Marvelous motion*. Edina, MN: Magic Wagon.
Summary: Colorful cartoonish illustrations introduce the basics of forces and motion.

Lindeen, M. 2017. *Speed*. Chicago: Norwood House Press.
Summary: This Beginning-to-Read book provides simple text and photographs that give kid-friendly examples of how to speed things up or slow them down.

Stille, D. R. 2004. *Motion: Push and pull, fast and slow*. North Mankato, MN: Picture Window Books.
Summary: Simple text and vivid illustrations offer an introduction to basic force and motion concepts, such as inertia, gravity, and friction.

Name: _____

Ride, Newton, Ride!

Part A: Low and High Ramps

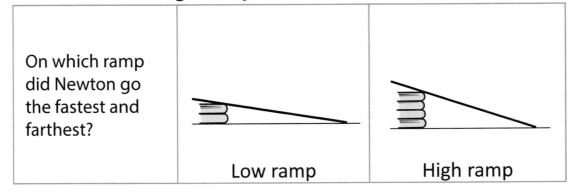

| On which ramp did Newton go the fastest and farthest? | Low ramp | High ramp |

Part B: Changing the Surface

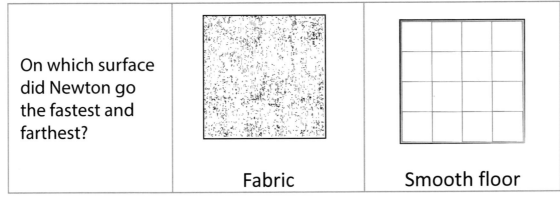

| On which surface did Newton go the fastest and farthest? | Fabric | Smooth floor |

Part C: Light Weight Versus Heavy Weight

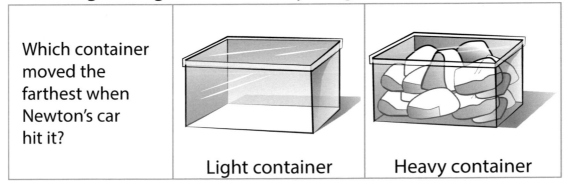

| Which container moved the farthest when Newton's car hit it? | Light container | Heavy container |

Name: _____

Our Best Design

How did you get Newton's car into the doghouse? Draw and label your best solution in the box below.

Name: _____

STEM Everywhere

Dear Families,

At school, we have been learning about **forces and motion**—the ways *pushes* and *pulls* can stop and start motion as well as change an object's direction. We experimented with a toy dog named "Newton" and a toy car. To find out more, ask your learner the following questions and discuss their answers:

- What did you learn?
- What was your favorite part of the lesson?
- What are you still wondering?

At home, you can test different objects to compare how they move down a ramp. To build a ramp, you will need something to prop up one end (like a stack of books) and a large flat piece of wood or cardboard (like a cutting board or cookie sheet). Then, you can collect some small objects such as blocks, paper tubes, and balls and check (✓) whether they **roll**, **slide**, or **stay in place** when released from the top of the ramp.

Predict, Then Try It!

Object	Rolls	Slides	Stays in Place